GH01018367

Henr⁣ ⁣y

Machine builder

K.R. Gilbert
M.A., D.I.C.

Her Majesty's
Stationery Office
London 1971

H. MAUDSLAY.

1 Portrait by H.Grevedon, 1827.
  Reversed photograph of the original lithographic stone

Henry Maudslay

'The successful construction of all machinery depends on the perfection of the tools employed; and whoever is a master in the arts of tool-making possesses the key to the construction of all machines . . . The contrivance and construction of tools must therefore ever stand at the head of the industrial arts'. Thus wrote Charles Babbage in 1851. The great impetus to machine-tool invention and to precision working in metals beyond the small-scale work of the instrument maker and the watchmaker came from the Industrial Revolution. The mechanisation of industry which had begun in the 1770's with Arkwright's cotton mills could not proceed further without machine shop technology; and the availability of driving power in the factories offered by Watt's rotative steam engine stimulated the invention of production machinery, which needed machine tools for its construction. The satisfaction of this need at the appropriate time was due primarily—to quote Nasmyth—'to Henry Maudslay, whose useful life was enthusiastically devoted to the grand object of improving our means of producing perfect workmanship and machinery'.

The chief source of contemporary information on Maudslay is James Nasmyth, who in 1829 at the age of 20 became his personal assistant and remained with him for the last two years of Maudslay's life. Nasmyth's reminiscences are contained in the *Autobiography* and it was he who provided most of the material used by Smiles for the chapter on Maudslay in his *Industrial Biography*, who, however, obtained additional information from Maudslay's partner, Joshua Field. Maudslay's work on screw cutting was also described at some length by Charles Holtzapffel.

Unfortunately Nasmyth, lacking the historical knowledge available today, made claims for Maudslay as the inventor of the slide-rest and the screw-cutting lathe, which can no longer be sustained. Maudslay himself made no such claims, as can be seen from the fact that his six patents do not include one on machine tools. Nevertheless later writers have followed Nasmyth. In recent times, however, Maudslay's contributions to work-shop technology have been critically re-assessed.

When Maudslay's Works closed down in 1900 several small but historically important tools and models were purchased by the Science Museum and other Maudslay items were later presented by his descendants. The other early machine tools were sold and presumably scrapped except for a fairly large lathe, which is now at the Henry Ford Museum, Dearborn, Michigan. A few of the other machines were described and illustrated in *Engineering* in 1901. It is there stated that Maudslay's own bench lathe was acquired by someone for preservation, but it is not now known what has become of it. All the records of the firm were regrettably destroyed at that time, but a certain amount of information on Maudslay and about the history of the firm after his death is now known due to the researches of J. Foster Petree.

Henry Maudslay was born at Woolwich on 22 August 1771. He was the son of Henry Maudsley, an ex-soldier from Clapham, Yorkshire, who, though baptised Maudsley, signed his marriage certificate as Maudslay, a spelling which his son retained. Henry senior had served in the Royal Artillery as a wheelwright and, having been severely wounded, was discharged from the army and was then employed as a storekeeper at Woolwich Dockyard until his death in 1780. His son, the engineer, was only 12 years old when he obtained his first employment: filling cartridges at Woolwich Arsenal.

After two years he was transferred to the carpenter's shop, but he was much more interested in blacksmith's work and managed when nearly 15 to move to the smithy, where he worked for three years, becoming an uncommonly skilful smith. His love of iron forging led him in later life to keep a stock of lead bars in his private workshop with which he could make models of work ultimately to be done in iron, cold lead being of about the same malleability as red hot iron. In this way he would work out how a difficult forging could best be done. It was at Woolwich presumably where he acquired his outstanding skill as a metal worker, about which one of his old workmen informed Smiles: 'It was a pleasure to see him handle a tool of any kind, but he was quite splendid with an eighteen inch file'. The set square, calipers and scribing block illustrated in plate 2 were doubtless made by him at this time.

Maudslay acquired such a reputation as a craftsman that a workman at Moodie's Smithy in Whitechapel, who had been consulted by Joseph Bramah, recommended him to seek the assistance of Maudslay, then only 18, in the manufacture of his patent lock. Bramah had invented in 1784 an ingenious lock, which is for practical purposes unpickable. One was exhibited in Bramah's shop window in Piccadilly in 1794 with a notice offering £200 to anyone who should succeed in picking it. There it remained until 1851 when the American locksmith Hobbs succeeded in opening it only after 16 days manipulation with various instruments. This lock, which is now in the Locks and Fastenings Collection of the Science Museum, was the work of Maudslay himself. Bramah's problem was to manufacture the lock accurately and economically and Maudslay's suggestions to this end were so sensible that Bramah engaged him. According to John Farey, who had known Bramah, writing in 1849; 'The secret workshops . . . contained several curious machines, for forming parts of the locks, with a systematic perfection of workmanship, which was at that time unknown in similar mechanical arts. These machines had been constructed by the late Mr Maudslay, with his own hands, while he was Mr Bramah's chief workman . . .'

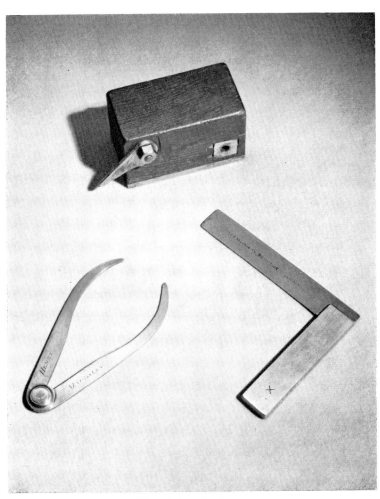

2　*Maudslay's set square, scribing block, and calipers*

3 *Spring winding machine*

From this factory there still survive in the Science Museum a sawing machine, spring winding machine, quick grip vice, milling cutters, and drilling templates.

The spring winding machine (plate 3) is of particular interest in that it is made on the lines of a screw-cutting lathe, driven by treadle and fly wheel, and having a saddle which travels the entire length of the bed, being drawn by a lead-screw. The lead-screw is driven from a headstock by change gears which permit the relative speeds of headstock rotation and saddle travel to be varied. Instead of a cutting tool, however, the saddle carries a reel of wire, which is wound onto an arbor held between centres, so forming a long spring, which was cut into the short lengths used in the lock.

The sawing machine was used for cutting slots in the lock barrels at precise angles. The machine has a massive wooden frame in which is mounted the indexing barrel holder and adjustable V-slides of brass to guide the saw frame. Bramah had patented his hydraulic press in 1795, but it was not properly effective because of the difficulty of preventing water from leaking past the piston. Maudslay again came to the rescue with his self-tightening leather collar.

In 1793 Maudslay had married Bramah's housekeeper, Sarah Tindale, and in 1797 with an increasing family to support he applied to his employer for an increase in his salary, which was then 30 shillings per week. Bramah curtly refused. So Maudslay, then aged 26, left and set up in business on his own account in a workshop and smithy at 64, Wells Street, off Oxford Street. His first customer was an artist, who gave him an order for the iron work of an easel of new design. Other orders followed and, as Maudslay became widely known as a first class workman, he soon became fully occupied. In 1802 he had to move to larger premises nearby at 78, Margaret Street, where he eventually employed 80 men.

The excellence of Maudslay's work resulted from the use of the lathes which he designed and his practice of workshop management. His lathes were made of metal, which gave rigidity without excessive bulk and enabled iron and steel workpieces to be machined. Furthermore it was possible with metal to obtain very flat surfaces which allowed close fitting and accurate adjustment. Although the small machine tools used by clockmakers in the preceding century and earlier had been made of metal, and metal was liberally used in the costly ornamental turning lathes used by amateurs for machining ivory and boxwood, the industrial lathe was framed in wood with only the centres and tool rest of iron. The workman applied and guided the cutting tool by muscular strength and the finish obtained depended entirely on his skill and dexterity.

The Maudslay bench lathe shown in plate 4 has his typical triangular bar bed, which rests on two standards and fits into triangular holes in the bridge-shaped castings of the headstock. The mandrel, which carries the chuck, has a 5-step cone pulley driven ultimately by the treadle. The

4   *Bench lathe, 1812-1820*

5   *Headstock and slide-rest of bench lathe*

tailstock rests on the triangular bed, to which it is clamped. The back bearing of the mandrel is tapered and adjustable lengthwise, as is the tailstock bearing. The slide-rest ordinarily fits on the bed, and is shown here (plate 5) mounted upon an adaptor which protrudes from the bed at right angles.

The slide-rest is a device for holding and guiding the cutting tool mechanically. The tool holder is carried on two slides one above the other and each is adjustable by a screw handle. The upper slide can also be set at any angle to the lower slide. The settings of the two screws determine the position of the tool, so that the workman has only to make these adjustments and is relieved of the strenuous and difficult task of guiding the tool manually. Maudslay has been credited with the invention of the slide-rest chiefly due to the enthusiastic advocacy of Nasmyth, though when evidence to the contrary was adduced by John Anderson, head of the Machinery Department at Woolwich Arsenal, he moved to the view that 'Maudslay must still stand as the parent of its introduction to the workshops of England'. This view finds support in the earliest printed reference to Maudslay, which appeared in 1806 in Olinthus Gregory's *A Treatise of Mechanics*. In the article on *Turning* the lathe manufactured by Maudslay is illustrated and described with the comment 'For turning faces of wheels, hollow work, &c., where great accuracy is wanted, Mr Maudslay has contrived a curious apparatus which he calls a slide-tool, ...'. In fact the slide-rest has a long history, for the earliest illustration of one is in the *Mittelalterliche Hausbuch*, a German manuscript of *c* 1480. Vaucanson in France by about 1760 had built a lathe which not only has a slide-rest, but is substantially constructed in the form of a framework

6   *Original screw-cutting lathe, c 1797*

of iron bars of square section. It can be assumed that Maudslay did not know of these and other foreign machines, but it is very probable that he was familiar with the gun boring machines at Woolwich Arsenal installed by the Dutch gun founder Jan Verbruggen and his son Peter in 1770, even if they were unknown to his contemporaries outside the arsenal. One of these machines, as is known from Peter Verbruggen's drawing of c 1780 and from a contemporary model, had a slide-rest to enable the exteriors of the gun barrels to be machined. It was this model that Anderson had brought to the attention of Smiles after the publication of the first edition of *Industrial Biography*. The original model was destroyed in World War 2, but the Science Museum fortunately has a copy of it.

Slide-rests were also fitted to the ornamental turning lathes used by amateurs in the 18th century, and indeed the late 17th century lathe exhibited in the Science Museum has one. Bramah had a lathe designed in 1794 either by him or by Maudslay of rather limited applicability in that the slide-rest was part of the tailstock.

Maudslay's original screw-cutting lathe (plate 6) constructed soon after he became independent in 1797 has a slide-rest with a graduated dial, which enabled the depth of cut to be determined. The lathe was preserved in Maudslay's works until they closed down, and was seen by the American engineer G.E. Sellers, when he visited the works in 1832. He wrote: 'Mr Field met us very cordially; showed us the collection of Mr Maudslay's own handwork that had been carefully preserved. The most interesting was his work in producing a standard screw, and his original screw-cutting lathe, said to be the father of all lathes, that by a combination of gear wheels and one guide screw any variety of pitch could be produced'.

The bed is 3 ft long and consists of two triangular bars secured at a fixed distance apart and supported on feet by which it was secured to a bench. A nut below the slide-rest is threaded on a lead-screw 1 in diameter by $\frac{1}{4}$ in pitch geared to the headstock spindle through change wheels, which are now missing. Various screws could be cut by employing different combinations of change wheels, but the unusual mounting of the lead-screw enabled it to be changed very readily and thus a much wider range of screws to be cut. The use of a lead-screw combined with change wheels in a screw-cutting machine was first proposed by Leonardo da Vinci in about 1500 and was used in a specialised clockmaker's machine tool, called a fusee engine, described by Antoine Thiout in 1741. Maudslay's contemporaries, Senot in France in 1795 and David Wilkinson in America in 1798 also built similar screw-cutting lathes, except that Wilkinson's machine was capable only of reproducing screws of the same pitch as the lead-screw.

The ability to make accurate screws is of the greatest importance in the production of machine tools and much other machinery, since screws

7 *Universal chuck, showing jaws and rear adjustment*

are used to bring about the controlled movement of one part of a machine relative to another. One application of a screw has already been seen in the construction of the slide-rest. Another example is in Maudslay's universal chuck (plate 7), in which the two jaws are moved evenly together or apart by a screw with right- and left-handed sections. By attaching a circular scale to a screw the amount by which it advances when it is turned, is known, so that *manual* skill in adjusting a cutting tool, for instance, is replaced by precise *mechanical* setting. The screw with an attached scale is also the essential element of a micrometer for the determination of length.

Early in the 19th century Maudslay constructed with the utmost care the bench micrometer (plate 8), which served as the ultimate standard in his workshops. He considered it as a Court of Final Appeal and called it 'The Lord Chancellor'. The micrometer consists of a gun-metal bed on which slide two saddles fitted with end-measuring faces and also having bevel-edged slots through which graduations on the bed can be read. One of the saddles extends through the bed and forms a split nut, which can be delicately tightened by set screws upon a horizontal lead-screw of 100 threads per inch. This screw has a collar on it that is held against a stationary abutment beneath the bed by a plate adjusted by screws so as

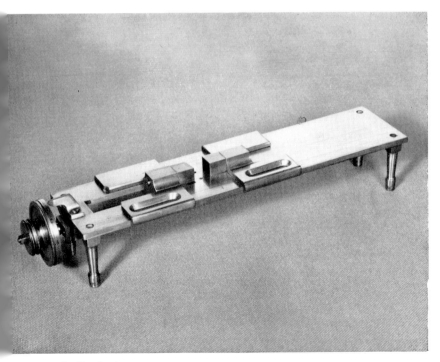

8 *Bench micrometer*

9 *Screw-cutting lathe, 1800*

to eliminate end play. The end of the lead-screw has a milled head with a graduated edge of 10 divisions each subdivided into 10, so that each subdivision indicates a saddle displacement of 0·0001 in. The idea of using a screw in measuring length was not Maudslay's, since a micrometer had been designed in the 17th century by William Gascoigne as part of a telescope eyepiece and a workshop micrometer graduated to 1/1800 in had been made by James Watt in *c* 1770.

Such screws could have been made on Maudslay's small screw-cutting lathe of instrument maker size (plate 9). It is now mounted on a cabinet which bears a brass label inscribed 'H. Maudslay 1800'—and contains cutting tools, change wheels, and samples of screws ranging from 16 to 100 threads per inch. The lead-screw of the lathe is mounted independently of the slide-rest low down in the frame and is connected with it by a form of split nut. The slide-rest also carries an adjustable stay to prevent springing of the rod being screwed. The lathe has flat guideways mounted on a substantial cast iron bed and resembles more the later industrial lathe than the earlier screw-cutting lathe (plate 6). This small lathe was hand driven, but Maudslay later built a screw-cutting lathe to be driven by steam power. These screw-making machines employed lead-screws and depended, of course, on the existence of an original screw. The methods available for originating screws reduced basically to three. The ancient method described by Hero of Alexandria consisted of wrapping a metal template round a cylinder of wood and using this to scribe a helix. The thread was then cut by chisel and file between the turns of the helix. There then followed a somewhat lengthy procedure for producing a corrected screw from this one. A second method employed the clockmaker's inclined plane fusee engine.

To quote Holtzapffel 'The late Mr Henry Maudslay devoted an almost incredible amount of labour and expense to the amelioration of screws and screwing apparatus, which as regarded the works of the millwright and engineer, were up to that time in a very imperfect state . . . in fact every scheme that he could devise, which appeared likely to benefit the result, was carefully tried, in order to perfect to the utmost the helical character and equality of subdivision of the screw'. The third method, eventually favoured by Maudslay, was mechanical and very direct (plate 10). A cylinder of hard wood or soft metal is placed with sliding fit inside a metal tube mounted in an open box carrying the various adjustments. There is a slot in the tube through which a crescent-shaped knife can be brought to bear on the cylinder obliquely to its axis. If the cylinder is rotated, the knife causes it to travel through the tube and incises a helix in the surface. Through a hole further along the tube a cutter is inserted which deepens the groove, so that a thread is obtained, which can be further deepened in several passes. The beautifully made apparatus (plate 11) is provided with the fine adjustments for helix angle, cutter position, and knife and cutter feeds. Having produced a satisfactory

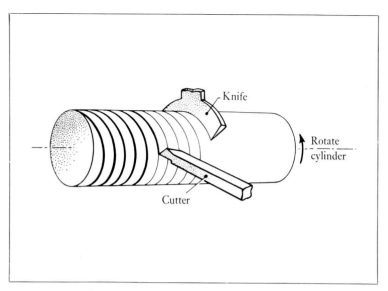

10   Principle of the screw originating machine

11   Screw originating machine, c 1800

screw by this means, Maudslay used it as a master in a screw-cutting lathe to produce another screw in steel. Nasmyth recorded that his first task, in 1829, was to assist Maudslay in making some modifications in the details of the originating machine. It became 'in the hands of its inventor the parent of a vast progeny of perfect screws, whose descendants, whether legitimate or not, are to be found in every workshop throughout the world, where first class machinery is constructed. The production of perfect screws was one of Maudslay's highest ambitions and his principal technical achievement'.

Maudslay also designed a screw-correcting lathe to produce screws of very small differences of pitch from an otherwise perfect master without having to use gears with impracticably large numbers of teeth such as 500 and 501, where a 1:500 correction was required. The cutter was attached to the short arm of a 10:1 lever, the fulcrum was attached to the nut on the lead-screw and the end of the long arm was constrained to travel along a bar inclined at a small adjustable angle to the lead-screw. In this way the cutter and the nut travelled at slightly different rates and a screw of the desired pitch was cut. What was perhaps Maudslay's masterpiece was exhibited at the Society of Arts. It was a screw 5 ft long, 2 in in diameter and had 50 turns per inch—i.e. 3,000 in all. On it was screwed a nut 12 in long with 600 threads, long enough for local variations in pitch to be averaged out. It was used in an apparatus for dividing scales for astronomical and other metrical purposes.

An outstanding feature of Maudslay's workshop practice was the production of accurate plane surfaces which are essential for the guide ways of machine tools and for engine valve faces. A metal surface having been made as flat as possible by the skilful use of a file, it was checked by bringing it into contact with a standard plane surface lightly smeared with oil containing red lead. This adhered to the high points, which were thus revealed so that they could be reduced by hard steel scrapers.

The original standard planes or surface plates were made three at a time and brought to perfection by testing each against the other two. The reason for making three surfaces coincide is that, with two only, one might be convex and the other concave, but if a third surface can be made to coincide with the first two, all three must be plane. According to Nasmyth this procedure was 'a very old mechanical dodge'. Maudslay however achieved his accurate plane surface by scraping, instead of by the earlier method of grinding, which was not capable of precision until much later. He regarded the production of true plane surfaces as essential and accordingly had surface plates placed on the benches beside his workmen so that they might test their work.

Maudslay also simplified the running of his workshop by standardising the nuts and screws used as fasteners in the assembly of machinery. The pitch and form of the threads in relation to the diameter was systematised. According to Holtzapffel 'He also effected a great many improvements in

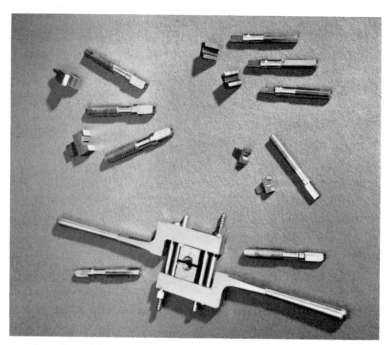

12   Taps, dies and diestock

the system of taps and dies, by which they were made to *cut* instead of *squeeze*: as to him are due the introduction of the three cutting edges and the division of the taps into the series of three namely: the entering or taper tap, the middle, and the plug tap, by which shallow holes or dead holes in cast iron can be safely tapped with full threads, a matter before impossible'. A selection of screwing tackle from the private workshop is shown in plate 12.

Marc Isambard Brunel had already by 1800 devised a scheme for the mass production of ship's pulley blocks, which were then used in large quantities by the Royal Navy. To interest block manufacturers in his proposals he decided to commission models of his machines. A fellow refugee from revolutionary France, M de Bacquancourt, who was an amateur turner and knew Maudslay and his work, recommended him to Brunel as a possible model maker. So Brunel went to Maudslay's shop, showed him a drawing and, not wishing at this stage to disclose the object he had in view, made a guarded enquiry for a model. On a subsequent visit Brunel produced another drawing. Thereupon Maudslay said 'Ah! now I see what you are thinking of; you want machinery for making blocks!' This convinced Brunel of Maudslay's understanding and ability to undertake the work, so he placed an order for the eight working models, which are now exhibited in the National Maritime Museum. Brunel failed to interest the principal block manufacturer in his scheme,

13   Maudslay lathe at the Henry Ford Museum, Dearborn, Mich., U.S.A.

but the Inspector-General of Naval Works, General Bentham, was convinced of its value and on his recommendation the Admiralty decided to install a set of machinery at Portsmouth Dockyard. In 1802 Maudslay was given the order for constructing the machinery, a task which occupied him until 1809.

The Portsmouth block-making machinery was the first large-scale plant to employ machine tools for mass production. It is unnecessary to relate here the history and mode of operation of the machinery, as this forms the subject of a Science Museum monograph.* The plant originally comprised 45 machines of 22 different kinds, so well constructed that most of them remained in use for nearly a century and a half. Apart from two large sawing machines, the machinery was constructed of metal, which enabled a great improvement in rigidity and accuracy to be obtained; whereas in earlier machinery metal had been used only sparingly for such parts as cutters and screws, the framing being of wood. Although according to Nasmyth, Maudslay 'designed for the most part this wonderful and complete series of machines', there is now no doubt that the design, down to quite small details, was the work of Brunel. It is nevertheless almost certainly the case that no one but Maudslay would at that time have been capable of building the machinery, and so both men

*The Portsmouth Block-making Machinery, K.R. Gilbert. 1965. HMSO.

14   Mortising machine, 1803, designed by M.I. Brunel, built by Maudslay

were fortunate in their collaboration. Maudslay thereby established his reputation as a machine builder and Nasmyth was right in saying that the experience which he (Maudslay) had thus obtained formed the foundation of his engineering fortune.

The characteristic style of Maudslay's subsequent machinery clearly derives from the block-machines. The classical columns supporting the overhead gear of the bench lathe (plate 4) and in the superstructure of the table engine (plate 15), and the cross bracing of the bases of the larger machine tools (plate 13) are already evident in the cast iron framing of Brunel's mortising machine of 1803 (plate 14). This machine was the largest machine tool—the flywheel is $6\frac{1}{2}$ft in diameter—to have been constructed entirely of metal up to that date. It was in use until 1948.

The order for the block-making machinery was the occasion that necessitated the move to larger premises in Margaret Street and for Maudslay to increase his staff, notably by the employment in 1804 of Joshua Field (1786-1863), a draughtsman at Portsmouth Dockyard, who later became his partner.

Olinthus Gregory in 1806 referred to the large lathes 'which Mr Maudslay uses in his manufactory' as being driven by a great wheel turned by two men; but this was an obviously inadequate source of motive power for the work in progress and Maudslay installed a 4hp steam engine.

Simon Goodrich, the Mechanist or engineer in charge at Portsmouth Dockyard, records in his journal a visit that he paid on 30 January 1807 to the works: 'Maudslay was not at home when I called—went round with young Field. Maudslay keeps making improvements to shop—His 4 horse steam engine made by Murray & Co is now fixed in his cellar and at work in fine order, it drives all his lathes, etc . . . Maudslay has added a small iron foundry to his premises a very great convenience for casting his own iron work—He has lately completed a large stamping press for his own use in which he stamps or cuts out teeth of circular saws which he has undertaken to manufacture in a manner superior to the common. A dividing apparatus is attached to this press by which any number of teeth are very accurately divided off as they are cut out—the superior quality of the saws is to depend on his superior management of hardening and tempering of them.' Goodrich also noted that Maudslay was engaged in making machinery for Brunel for the manufacture of veneers.

At about this time Maudslay invented the table engine, a type of steam engine taking little floor space and suitable for driving machinery. The engine was patented in 1807 and by 1815 the design represented by the contemporary model (plate 15) had been evolved. The drawing by Field (plate 16) shows the internal arrangement.

The cylinder is carried vertically on a cast-iron table, beneath which are the crank-shaft bearings and the condensing arrangements. The piston rod passes through the top cover and terminates in an equalising cross-

15 *Table engine, model, 1815*

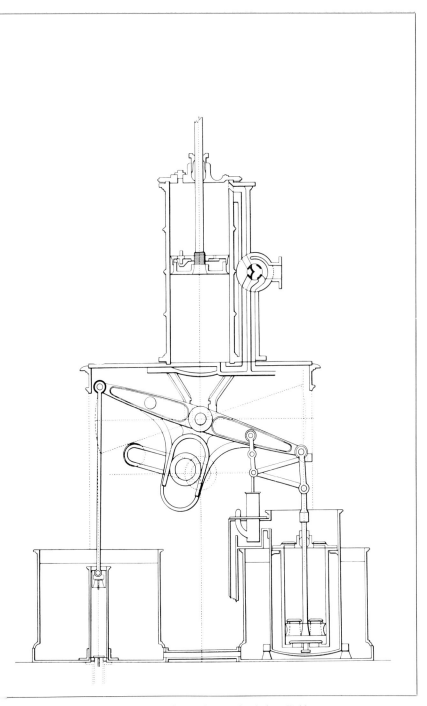

16   *Table engine, redrawn from a drawing by Joshua Field*

17   *Calico printing machine, model, 1805*

18   *The Works of Maudslay, Sons & Field, c 1840 (Transactions of the Newcomen Society, X*

head carrying a pair of wheels, which roll between guides formed in an independent framing secured to the table and the cylinder. From the cross head there are two connecting rods, which descend to two independent cranks in the crank shaft below. The steam is distributed by a 4-way plug cock rocked by a rod connected with a triangular cam on the crank shaft. The air, cold water, and feed pumps are worked by an inverted T bob driven by a roller on the intermediate portion of the crank shaft.

Many engines of the type were made in the next half century. One of them is to be seen in the Science Museum's Model of an Engineering Workshop, which was commenced in 1849. Maudslay sold a 6hp engine to the Royal Arsenal at Woolwich in 1809 for £645 and an 8hp engine in 1814 to the Conservatoire des Arts et Métiers, Paris. He later installed three table engines in his own works, and two of them were still driving some of the machinery until 1900.

Maudslay was also interested in calico printing machinery and took out patents in 1805 and 1808. His model is shown in plate 17. The engraved copper plate is supported on a table, which is lifted by two eccentrics on a horizontal shaft and powerfully pressed upwards against the calico, which rests under a flat platen. There are three blanket rollers, the upper one of which is in adjustable guides, while the front one is fluted and receives a periodical feed motion by intermittent gearing driven from the eccentric shaft; so that after every impression the calico is carried through by the blanket a distance equal to the width of the block. The frame carrying the printing plate is in duplicate and hinged, so that while one plate is printing the other is being inked, possibly in a different colour. The machine appears to have achieved considerable success until it was superseded by the cylindrical form.

Maudslay's other patents were with Bryan Donkin in 1806 for a differential gear hoist; with Robert Dickinson in 1812 for a method of sweetening water by aeration; and with Field in 1824 for changing the water in marine boilers.

In 1810 Maudslay transferred his rapidly expanding business to Lambeth Marsh, and started to build his new works on land unoccupied save for the buildings of a former riding school. The frontage in Westminster Bridge Road, as it appeared in 1840, is shown in plate 18. The office block is in the centre, Maudslay lived in the house on the left and Field in the left of the pair of houses on the right. On the extreme right is the classical façade of the front erecting shop. The site of Maudslay's house and of the offices is now occupied by Lambeth North Underground Station. In 1826 Thomas Allen in his book *The Parish of Lambeth* referred to 'the extensive factory of Messrs Maudslay's, supposed to be the most complete in the kingdom. Steam engines, tanks for shipping, and all works connected with various factories, are here executed in the best manner. They occasionally employ upwards of two hundred men'.

A report on Maudslay's Works published in 1833 in the Proceedings of the Verein zur Beförderung des Gewerbfleisses in Preussen, a Berlin society which in 1829 had elected Maudslay to honorary membership, has an illustration (plate 19) of the Main Erecting Shop as it appeared in 1830. It shows the erection of a marine engine in progress: a cylinder is being lifted by a movable floor crane with a counterbalance weight hanging from the other jib. Already in 1813 Maudslay had informed Goodrich that he had an improved floor crane capable of lifting 10 tons and employing iron instead of wood. Situated in the left foreground is a table engine which was available for use in the Erecting Shop, but which was principally used for driving machine tools in the adjoining workshop.

A piston with piston rod stands on a trolley on the right, behind it is another trolley carrying a crankshaft, and resting on the floor is one of the side levers. On reference to plate 21 it is apparent that the engine depicted in plate 19 and on the cover is the engine pair which was later installed in the paddle steamer DEE, about which Nasmyth wrote 'They formed a noble object in the great erecting shop'.

The building measured 148 ft × 55 ft and the walls were 20 ft in height. The roof was one of the earliest examples of the use of cast iron for such a structure. The roof covering, which is not shown in place, was of iron plates. The roof was probably constructed in 1826 to replace the first roof, which collapsed during erection on 24 May. The second roof structure was satisfactory and remained without alteration until the building was demolished in 1900.

Maudslay remained the sole proprietor of the business until 1812 when 'H. Maudslay & Co' was formed by Henry Maudslay; his eldest son, Thomas Henry Maudslay; Joshua Field; and John Mendham, Mrs Field's uncle. The date is presumed from the advertising circular (plate 20), which is watermarked '1812' and is the earliest reference to the Company. The circular shows a sectioned engine house containing a beam engine and boiler and states that 'Henry Maudslay & Co, Engineers, London, beg leave respectfully to acquaint Gentlemen, Merchants, Manufacturers and their Agents, that they are enabled by their extensive Manufactory and Machinery at Lambeth, to furnish (upon reasonable terms) the most approved and complete Steam Engines, & when to send abroad provided with all necessary duplicates &c. of the wearing parts to ensure their perfect success in countries where mechanical assistance cannot easily be procured. They also beg leave to state that they keep on Stock small Engines and the principal parts of those larger powers most in demand that an order may be executed at the shortest notice. Millwork, Water Works & Machinery of every kind executed in their usual style of workmanship.'

In 1820 Mendham retired and the remaining partners continued as 'Maudslay, Son & Field' until January 1831, when Maudslay's third son, John, and fourth son, Joseph, joined the Company, which

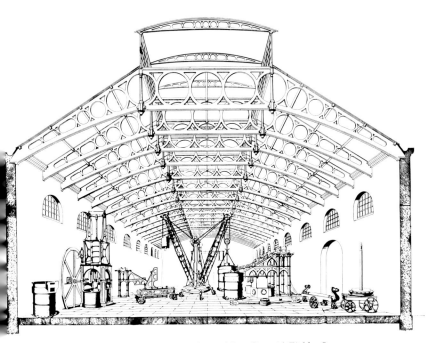

19   The Main Erecting Shop of Maudslay, Sons & Field, 1830

Henry Maudslay & Co. Engineers, London.

beg leave respectfully to acquaint Gentlemen, Merchants, Manufacturers
and their Agents that they are enabled by their extensive Manufactory
at Machinery at Lambeth to furnish (upon reasonable terms) the
most approved and complete Steam Engines & when to send abroad
provided with all necessary duplicates &c, of the wearing parts to ensure
their perfect success in countries where mechanical assistance cannot easily be procured.

   They also beg leave to state that they keep in Stock small
Engines and the principal parts of those larger powers most in demand
that an order may be executed at the shortest notice.

   Mill work, Water Works & Machinery of every kind executed
in their usual style of workmanship.

20   Advertising circular, 1812

then assumed the well-known name 'Maudslay, Sons & Field.' As such the Company continued, with the addition of 'Ltd' in 1869, until its dissolution at the end of the century.

The Company became renowned as Marine Engineers, but its practice in general engineering was extensive both in Maudslay's lifetime and later. Maudslay had supplied saw mill machinery to the Woolwich Arsenal in 1808 and in 1814 Field sent an estimate to Colonel Pilkington for re-equipping the boring mills with steam-driven machinery writing 'I have accordingly prepared a plan of a boring mill which embraces all those improvements which long and extensive practice in the art of turning have enabled me to make'. The equipment costing £6,780 included a 30hp engine, 8 lathes for the boring room, and 3 rougher lathes for the turning room. The mention of lathes is interesting because in spite of Maudslay's great contributions to machine shop technology there is little evidence that he manufactured machine tools for sale. The lathe shown in plate 4, labelled *H. Maudslay & Co. fecerunt London*, was not intended for industrial use. The elegant framing and cabinet make it suitable for a gentleman's workshop and the lathe was manufactured for amateur turners at the price of £200. A bench lathe of similar capacity but with a workaday cabinet, and intended for clockmakers, instrument makers and similar craftsmen, has been preserved and belongs to the Science Museum's Circulation Collection. The bed is inscribed with the words *H. Maudslay fecit London.*

The firm supplied gun-boring machinery to Brazil in 1813, constructed a Congreve's patent lock for the Regent's Canal in 1814, hydraulic presses for Cockerill of Liège in 1819, the shield and pumping equipment for Brunel's Thames Tunnel in 1825, punching and shearing machines for manufacturing water tanks, pumping engines for various undertakings, and bronze foundry equipment for Sir Francis Chantrey, the sculptor. The firm also throughout its career manufactured coin-minting machinery. The draw bench designed by Sir John Barton, the Deputy Controller of the Royal Mint, for reducing rolled fillets of gold and silver to exact size, was constructed by Maudslay in 1816. The machine, which increased the output of acceptable blanks by $5\frac{1}{2}$ per cent, is illustrated in *The Mint* by Sir John Craig (1953). It was clearly a machine in the style of the block-making machinery.

Maudslay's work in marine engineering began with the building in 1815 of the 17hp engine for the RICHMOND, the first steam passenger vessel to ply on the Thames. In Maudslay's lifetime the Company is known to have supplied machinery for 45 ships. These included, in 1823, HMS LIGHTNING, the first steam vessel in the Royal Navy; and in 1825, the ENTERPRISE, the first steam ship to make the passage to India.

In 1830 Maudslay commenced the construction of a pair of 200hp marine engines, the largest to date. His partners were rather opposed to so expensive an undertaking, as no order for them had been received.

The engines were eventually purchased by the Admiralty for the paddle steamer DEE, completed in 1832, a mail packet used for post office work. Maudslay was so pleased with the advanced design and great power of the engines that he personally constructed with the assistance of Nasmyth the very fine model illustrated in plate 21. It was for the purpose of making the large number of very small nuts and bolts required that Nasmyth invented a nut milling attachment for a lathe, which he later developed into a nut milling machine.

The side lever engines of the DEE had 54in diameter cylinders and 5ft stroke. They were an adaptation of the Boulton and Watt beam engine, in which the overhead beam was replaced by two beams, one on each side of the engine placed low down, with consequent saving of head room and improved stability of the vessel. The cast-iron framing of the engines is in the gothic revival style.

Another activity in the private workshop, as recorded by Nasmyth, was the building of model ship's hulls for testing their resistance to passage through water at different velocities. Maudslay intended by systematic experiment to determine the laws of resistance, so that the best hull shapes could be designed for the propulsive power available.

21   *Engines of the* P.S.DEE, *model, 1829*

There also he received his many distinguished friends who liked to call and spend much time discussing matters of current interest or reminiscing, without apparently interfering appreciably with the progress of work in hand. This circle of friends included Sir Samuel Bentham, Marc Brunel, Sir John Barton, Francis Chantrey, Bryan Donkin the engineer and inventor, and Michael Faraday.

If Maudslay was not alone in his day as a great mechanical engineer and manufacturer of machinery, for among his contemporaries were such men as Matthew Murray and James Fox, his influence was nevertheless pre-eminent not only through the activities of his own Company, but through the work and example of the many distinguished engineers, who were trained by him. Of his successors in the firm, Field was recognised as a leader of the engineering profession by his election to the Royal Society and was one of the founders of the Institution of Civil Engineers; and Joseph Maudslay became a distinguished marine engineer, having 22 patents to his credit.

Among those who worked at Maudslay's were: Joseph Clement, builder of precision machine tools; James Seaward, marine engine inventor; William Muir, machine tool manufacturer; Richard Roberts locomotive manufacturer and inventor of the self-acting spinning mule and of the first really satisfactory power loom; Joseph Whitworth, greatest British machine-tool manufacturer of the 19th century; and James Nasmyth, founder of an important engineering works and inventor of the steam hammer and of the shaping machine. These men used and disseminated the workshop techniques which Maudslay had employed to achieve the manufacture of accurate and reliable machinery, namely: absolute rigidity of construction, the production of true plane surfaces, the production of accurate screw threads, and the practice of frequent and precise measurement. It was therefore due primarily and in the greatest measure to Maudslay that England was able to become in the 19th century the 'Workshop of the World'.

Maudslay's appearance at the age of 56 is shown in plate 1. He was of commanding presence, a massive and portly man, 6ft 2in in height, with a good humoured face and keen bright eyes. He was good natured and had a cheerful ringing laugh, yet impressed with his force of character. His frank and cordial manner set everyone at ease at the first meeting. He had codified his experience into a set of maxims, which on appropriate occasions he was fond of bringing out, such as: 'Keep a sharp look-out upon your materials; get rid of every pound of material you can do without; put yourself the question "What business has it to be there?" avoid complexities, and make everything as simple as possible'.

'No one', it was said of him, 'could be more faithful and consistent in his friendships, nor more firm in the hour of adversity'. It was in response to the claims of friendship that he travelled in January 1831 to Boulogne to visit a friend, who was ill. He stayed there a week until assured of his friend's convalescence, but on his return voyage across the Channel, he caught a severe chill, which led to his death.

He was buried in the churchyard of St Mary's, Woolwich in a vault surmounted by a cast-iron tomb of his own design, commemorating many members of his family, including his parents.

The tomb survived the clearances at the end of the last century, when the churchyard became a public garden, but was demolished and cleared away by the local authority in 1966. It is most regrettable that the panel bearing Maudslay's epitaph in cast letters was then lost. The text of the inscription was probably composed by Joshua Field and read:

TO THE MEMORY OF

HENRY MAUDSLAY

BORN IN THIS PARISH 1771
DIED AT LAMBETH FEB 15TH 1831
A ZEALOUS PROMOTER
OF THE ARTS & SCIENCES
EMINENTLY
DISTINGUISHED AS AN
ENGINEER
FOR MATHEMATICAL
ACCURACY AND
BEAUTY OF CONSTRUCTION
AS A MAN FOR
INDUSTRY & PERSEVERANCE
AND AS A FRIEND FOR A KIND &
BENEVOLENT HEART

Bibliography

Smiles, Samuel. *Industrial Biography : Iron Workers and Tool Makers.* London. 2nd. ed. 1879.

Nasmyth, James. *An Autobiography.* London. 1883.

Holtzapffel, Charles. *Turning and Mechanical Manipulation.* Vol. 2. London. 1856.

Benson, W. A. S. The Early Machine Tools of Henry Maudslay. *Engineering.* London, 18 Jan. and 1 Feb., 1901.

Petree, J. Foster. *Henry Maudslay, 1771-1831 ; and Maudslay, Sons & Field, Ltd.* Publ. The Maudslay Society. 1949.

Petree, J. Foster. The Lambeth Works of Maudslay, Sons and Field. *The Engineer.* London. 8 June, 1934.

Petree, J. Foster. Maudslay, Sons & Field as General Engineers. *Transactions of the Newcomen Society.* XV. London. 1936.

Petree, J. Foster. 'Henry Maudslay—Pioneer of Precision' in *Engineering Heritage.* 1. London. 1964.

Woodbury, Robert S. *History of the Lathe to 1850.* Cleveland, Ohio. 1961.

Printed in England for Her Majesty's Stationery Office by Eyre and Spottiswoode Limited at Grosvenor Press Portsmouth
Dd 502179/K32